D1095492

THE BEAR WHO SAW THE SPRING

by KARLA KUSKIN

HARPER & ROW, PUBLISHERS
NEW YORK AND EVANSTON

LIBRARY
WESTERN OREGON STATE COLLEGE
MONMOUTH, OREGON 97361

FOR CHARLIE AND HIS NICHOLAS

JUV.
PN
6109.97
.K97
B36
1961

THE BEAR WHO SAW THE SPRING

Copyright © 1961 by Karla Kuskin

Printed in the United States of America

All rights in this book are reserved.
No part of the book may be used or reproduced
in any manner whatsoever without written per-
mission except in the case of brief quotations
embodied in critical articles and reviews. For
information address:
    Harper & Row, Publishers, Incorporated,
    49 East 33rd Street, New York 16, N. Y.

Library of Congress catalog card number: 60-11195

SPRING

This is a dog.
He sits alone
Beneath a tree
Upon a stone.

This dog
Is very young and small
And he has not seen much at all.

He likes to sit
And sniff the air.
He never has been anywhere.
He never has seen anything
Except one time of year,
The spring.

So everything he sees
Is new.
His name is Louis Dog
Or Lou.

One day
When Louis sat alone
Beneath a tree
Upon a stone,

An animal with thick brown hair
Walked up and said,
"I am a bear."

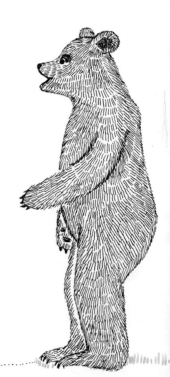

And Louis said,
"How do you do?
I thought you were a dog,"
Said Lou.

The bear sat down
Upon a log
And said,
"I'm bigger than a dog.
I'm fierce
And very furry too."
"Your voice is very deep,"
Said Lou.

"Yes I can growl
And I can roar,
And I have seen
The spring before.
And I have traveled
Very far,
And I am older than you are."

"Well, I am very young and small
And I have not seen much at all.
I hardly have seen anything.
Please tell me first
About the spring."

The bear said,
"Spring is green.
I mean, it's full of things
All turning green—
The grass, the buds,
The leaves on trees.
The sun is warm,
Please sniff the breeze."
And Louis sniffed.
"Ah, good," said he,
"Now I would like to see a tree."

"Here is a tree,"
The bear said.
"Let's climb awhile,"
Said he.
"The leaves are green and little
The way spring leaves will be.

"Here is a nest,"
The bear said.
"Birds make their nests
In spring
And then they lay
Their eggs in them
And sit on them
And sing."

"The nest is very funny,"
Said Louis, "like a hat.
And there is something
In the nest,"
Said Louis, "what is that?
And why does it
Just sit there
And never say a word?"

"That is an egg,"
The bear replied,
"And it will be a bird."

"But it is very quiet
And it is all alone.
I think that I will sit on it.
I think it is a stone."

"No," said the bear,
"That will not do.
The egg is small,
The egg is new,
And in a week
Or three or two,
As I have said,
As you have heard,
From inside out
Will come a bird.

"Here is a pond,"
The bear said.
"The water here is blue
And very good for drinking up."
Bear drank some.
Lou did too.

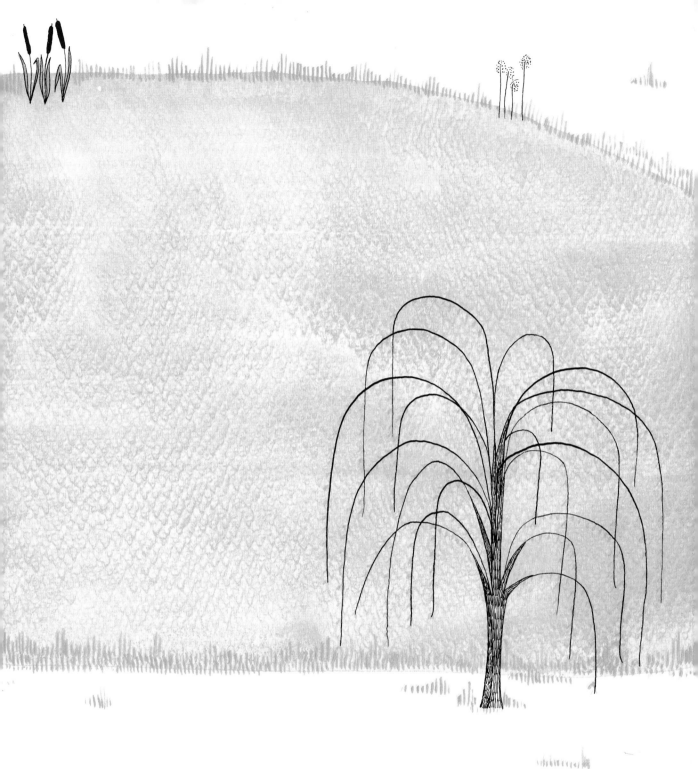

"Stare way down there,"
Said Lou to Bear,
While lapping up his drink.
"There's someone looking
Up at me
Who has a tail, I think."

"That is a tadpole,"
Said the bear.
"He likes to swim around
Down there."
"I thought he was a fish,"
Said Lou.
"He looks like one,"
Said Bear,
"Quite true.

"But as the grass gets greener
And grows around the bog,
His tail will go,
His legs will grow,
And he will be a frog.

"Here is a bud,"
The bear said.
"Is it to eat?"
Asked Lou.

"The bud is just to look at,
The bud is not to chew.
And as the grass grows greener,
The bud will bloom and be
A flower in a bower
Full of honey for the bee."

"Here's something like a ribbon
But it's moving," Louis said.
"And I think it has a lot of feet.
I think it has a head.
A ribbon doesn't look as fat.
A ribbon lies much stiller."
"Yes that is true,"
Said Bear to Lou,
"This is a caterpillar."
"A catter what?"
Said Louis Dog.
"I mean a catter who?
These catterwoolerpillars, Bear,
Please tell me what they do."

"A caterpillar nibbles leaves
And crawls from here to there
For it has many furry legs
That take it everywhere.

"But as the grass grows greener
And when the spring is over,
Then it will be a butterfly
And flutter over clover.
And it will fly to flowers
Through the sweet soft summer air."

"I like the spring,"
Said Louis.
"It is nice,"
Said the bear.

SUMMER

The day is warm.
The day is fair.
This is a dog.
This is a bear.

They sit beneath
A tall cool tree
And talk about
The things they see.

The dog is not
As young and small
As he was in the spring.
"I'm getting tall,"
Said Louis,
"And so is everything."

"Here is the tree,"
The bear said.
They climbed into the tree.
"The leaves are green
And thick and full
Of sun and shade,"
Said he.

"Here is the nest,"
The bear said.
"The egg is in the nest."
And Louis said,
"I've climbed enough.
Sit down here, Bear, and rest."

Just then there was
A little crack
And Louis gave a shout.
And then there was
Another crack
And something small came out.

"Here is a mouse,"
Said Louis.
"A mouse inside an egg.
He has a very funny face
And such a little leg."

"That is a bird,"
The bear said,
"And he is very new.
He looks the way
That all the other
Very new birds do."

"Then let us sit
And watch the bird,"
Said Louis to the bear.
And soon they saw
A bigger bird
Come flying through the air.

The big bird smiled
And said, "Small bird,
Here is a little treat.
It is a worm
And all for you.
A worm is good to eat."

The small bird
Was so very small
He did not say a word at all
But ate the worm
Without a peep
And then fell very fast asleep.

Louis asked,
"When will he fly?"
"When the grass is green and high
In a week or two
He will fly," the big bird said.
"I want to try," said Lou.

"A bird can't bark,"
The bear said,
"And it is true as well
A dog can't fly."
Said Lou, "I'll try."
He tried,
And down he fell.

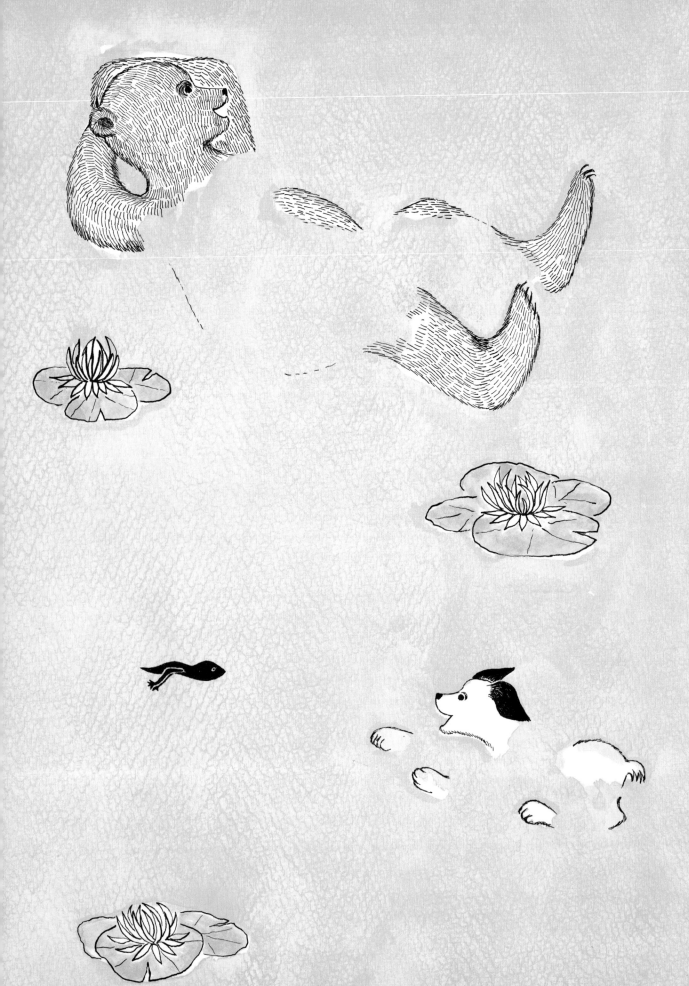

"Here is the pond,"
The bear said.
"The pond so cool and blue.
The pond is good for drinking up
And good for swimming too.

"The sun is hot in summer.
The pond is wet and cool."
Then Bear and Louis
Swam around
The good, wet, blue, cool pool.

The tadpole said,
"Hello there, Lou.
Do I look quite the same to you?

"You see that I have legs now
Where I had none before,
And I can go for little walks
And soon I will walk more.

"For as the grass grows greener
And higher round this bog,
I will be less and less a fish
And more and more a frog."

Then Lou and Bear
Lay on the grass.
The sun was hot and high.
They watched the white clouds
Drift and pass.
They saw a dragonfly.
They played "I Spy"
And Bear said, "I
Spy something round and blue.
It stands upon a grass green stalk,
It doesn't fly or swim or walk,
It doesn't sing,
It doesn't talk."
"Is it a bud?" asked Lou.

"In spring it was," the bear replied,
"Until its petals opened wide
And wider hour after hour,
And it bloomed into a flower."

Then Louis jumped
And said to Bear,
"A flower's flying through the air.
I wonder how,
I wonder why?"
And Bear said,
"That's a butterfly.

"The caterpillar ate awhile
And crawled awhile," Bear said.
"And then it curled into a ball
When it was fully fed
And there it stayed
And slowly changed
For a week or two.
And now it is a butterfly.
And that is how it grew,

"As everything grows up,"
Said Bear,
"The grass, the leaf, the tree,
The spring grows into summer
And I grow into me.

"As summer turns to autumn
And nights get cool and colder,
Everything grows up,"
Said Bear,
"And grows a little older."

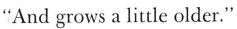

FALL

The day is cool.
The day is fair.
Here is a dog.
Here is a bear.
They listen to the kingbird call
And watch the summer
Turn to fall.

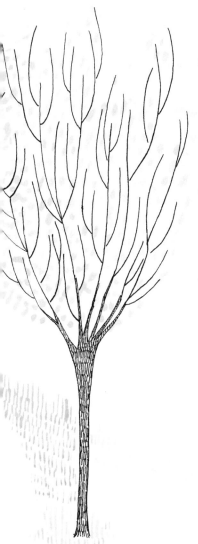

A leaf drifts
Through the autumn air
And settles on the nose of Bear.
"You've something
On your nose," said Lou.
"That's funny," Bear said,
"So do you."

"It is a leaf,"
The bear said.
"The leaves are gold and red
And as the wind wafts
Through the tree
The leaves drift down,"
He said.
"Are they to wear?" asked Louis,
And put them on his head.

Then Louis rolled and jumped in leaves
And arfed and bowed and wowed.
The bear said, "I like autumn too,
But must you bark so loud?

"Here is the nest,"
The bear said.
"Where is the bird?" said Lou.
"I am the bird," a bird said,
"And I am big and blue.
And I can fly and feed myself
And hop around and sing."
"And once you were an egg,"
Said Lou,
"And couldn't do a thing."

The bird flew up and over
Where the bear and Louis sat.
"An egg?" she said. "I was an egg?
I don't remember that."

"As spring turns into summer
And summer turns to fall,
Everyone who grows,"
Said Bear,
"Forgets that they were small.
And some forget a little.
And some forget a lot."
And Louis said, "Oh really, Bear,
You know that I shall not."

"Here is the pond,"
The bear said.
"I want to swim,"
Said Lou.
He quickly jumped into the pond.
He quickly jumped out too.
He stamped his paws
And shook his fur
And shivered
While he shouted, "Brrrr."

"Lou," said Bear,
"You ought to know
Pools get cool before the snow.

"Here is the frog,"
The bear said.
"Yes here I am," said Frog.
He jumped a stump
And with a thump
He landed on a log.
"My leaps are long,
My back is green,
My voice is loud and deep.
And in the rushy bog at night
I sing while others sleep."

Then Dog and Frog
Sat on a log
And croaked and barked a song.
"How fair," said Bear,
"How rich, how rare.
But isn't it too long?"

"From fish to tadpole
And to frog
You've changed
While living in this bog.
Why it was just last spring,"
Said Lou,
"I am amazed at how you grew."

"You mean," said Frog,
"I was so small
I could not lightly leap at all?"
He lightly leapt
And said to Dog,
"I thought I always
Was a frog."

"Look," said Louis sadly,
Sitting on the ground,
"The flower has been pulled apart
And scattered all around.
Maybe with some thread or glue
We could put it back,"
Said Lou.

The bear said, "No,"
And scratched his ear,
"The flower cannot bloom all year.

"The air is cool.
The tree is bare.
The petals settle here and there.
The deer are quick.
The small birds call.
These things happen every fall."

"It's very good to know,"
Said Lou,
"That next year there will be fall too."

WINTER

The day is cold.
Upon a log
There sit a pair,
A bear and dog.

"It's cold," said Lou.
"It is," said Bear.
"I'm glad," said Lou,
"I've hair to wear."
"And I am also glad," said Bear.

"Look," said Lou,
"At all that stuff.
I mean," he said,
"That white, that fluff,
Those little bits
That come and go."
And Bear said, "Oh,
You mean the snow.
Watch it whirl,"
The bear said.
"The first snow of the year.
It falls on pond and town and tree.
You have some on your ear."
Then Louis barked
And ran around
And said, "It's falling by the pound."

He chased his tail
And skipped and rolled
And said, "It's nice and white and cold
And deep and good for digging too.
I wish it snowed all year," said Lou.

"Where is the bird?" asked Louis.
"Has he seen the snow?"
"The bird has flown South,"
Said Bear.
"The South is where birds go.
When fall turns into winter
And skies go gray with storm
Then all the birds fly South,"
Said Bear.
"The South is where it's warm.

"Here is the pond," the bear said.
Lou looked and did not see it.
"We're walking on the pond," said Bear.
Said Lou, "This cannot be it.
I may not be as big as you.
I may not be as old.
But I know ponds are wet and soft
And this is hard and cold."

Said Bear to Lou,
"Yes that is true
When days are warm and nice
But as the winter wanders on
The water turns to ice.
When leaves are gone
And birds are flown
And hills wear hats of snow
We skip and slip and slide
On ice
On paw and tail and toe."

And Louis skipped and slipped and slid
As fast as he could go.

"The leaves are gone.
The bird has flown.
The snow is on the bog.
The ice is on the pond," said Lou.
"But where, Bear, is the frog?"
"Beneath the ice and snow,"
Said Bear, explaining it to Lou,
"The frog will sleep
In good warm mud
Until the winter's through."

"That means he cannot
Roll in snow
Or slide on ice,"
Said Lou.
"But frogs like mud the best,"
Said Bear,
"So that is what they do."

"The frog is sleeping
Warm and deep.
His blanket is of mud.
The bird has flown.
The leaves are gone.
But where, Bear, is the bud?"

"The bud has bloomed.
The bloom is gone.
And hour after hour
A seed sits underneath the snow.
The seed will be a flower.
Its root will root.
Its stem will shoot
When winter turns to spring.
And you and I shall wander by
And watch the pretty thing."

"The bird has flown.
The leaves are gone.
The frog sleeps in the mud.
The seed sits in the earth and waits
To grow into a bud.
The snow is crisp
Beneath our feet
As we go walking by.

"But tell me where,"
Said Lou to Bear,
"We'll find the butterfly?"

"He died," said Bear,
"Before the cold.
Most butterflies don't get too old."
And Lou said, "Bear,
When winter's done
Then will there be another one
To sit and swoop and flutter over
Purple strife and phlox and clover?"
"Of course," said Bear.
"That's always true."
"You know, I thought it was,"
Said Lou.

"Next spring," said Bear,
"There will be more
Of everything you've seen before.
You'll see the grass come up
And then
You'll watch the year go by again."
"That will be very nice," said Lou,
"But meanwhile there is snow to chew
And many winter things to do."

Then Bear said,
"Lou, I'll say good-by.
I have to find a cave that's dry
And snug and warm
Where I can yawn
And snore and sleep till winter's gone.
For when the snow is white and deep
We brown-haired bears
Fall fast asleep.

"Good night,"
Said Bear.
"I'll see you when
The warm spring air blows by again."
"Good night,"
Said Lou.
"I'll see you then."